W9-DJJ-378

蔡志忠漫画中英文版

老子说 ②

THE DAO SPEAKS Ⅱ

智·者·的·低·语

More Whispers of Wisdom

蔡志忠/著　BRIAN BRUYA〔美〕/译

现代出版社

Contents

Tsai Chih Chung (C. C. Tsai) is the most accomplished and popular cartoonist in all of East Asia, with parts of this series of his books having even been incorporated into the public school curriculum in Japan. C. C. Tsai began his career at the age of sixteen by publishing the first of what would be approximately 200 "action" comic books. Following that, he went into animation and garnered himself the equivalent of our Oscar while building up the largest animation company in Taiwan. In his spare time, he turned to the humor of comic strips and put out the first daily comic strip in Taiwan newspapers.

Then, one day on a flight to Japan, he began to sketch scenes from a book he was reading. The book had been written over two thousand years ago by one of the most influential thinkers in Chinese history, the famous Daoist (Taoist) named Zhuangzi (Chuang Tzu). From these sketches emerged a new genre in the book world—a serious (though light-hearted) comic book explicating a profound topic. C. C.'s aim was not to simplify, but to clarify. The ancient language in China is difficult for modern people to understand, so in addition to illustrating the subject matter, he also rendered the text into Modern Chinese.

When Zhuangzi Speaks came out in Taiwan, it shot to the top of the bestseller list, and the head of a major publishing company immediately remarked that it had world potential. Tired of animation by now, C. C. sold off his company and devoted all of his efforts to the daily comic strips and his new series on ancient Chinese thought, both of which were bringing him unparalleled fame for a cartoonist. Soon, he held the four highest spots atop the bestseller list, until other authors demanded that comic books no longer be allowed on the list of "serious literature". There are now over twenty books in C. C.'s series and millions of copies in print, and, just as predicted, they are rapidly gaining popularity all over the world.

The Dao Speaks is a close adaptation of a book known as the Dao De Jing, which is attributed to a mysterious figure known as Laozi. "Dao De Jing" literally means the Classic of the Way and the Virtue. In this book, the word "Dao" is used more in a metaphysical sense, as an insentient and unseen force or principle, than in the concrete (or metaphorical) sense of a pathway, and since there is no convenient English rendering of this sense of the word, I leave it simply as "the Dao". "De" on the other hand is a bit more complicated.

I translate "De" as "virtue", but the meanings of the words "De" and "virtue" are similar in more than just one sense. They both have the meanings of moral excellence according to a certain standard, yet there is still more to them than just this. In the Dao De Jing, "virtue" is used in a more metaphysical sense, as a kind of power of the Dao that nurtures or is immanent in all things. For this reason some translators have rendered it as "power" or "potency". Interestingly, if we look up "virtue" in the Oxford English Dictionary, the very first definition reads: "The power or operative influence in a supernatural or divine being." The dictionary reminds us that this is an archaic definition, but for purposes here, we will go back to it. Keep in mind, then, that virtue in the Dao De Jing means 1) moral excellence according to the standard of the Dao and 2) a kind of nurturing potency stemming from the Dao and inherent in all things. In Daoism, the most natural person is the most virtuous person.

Any reader who has come across Daoism before may be wondering why it is written here as "Dao" rather than the more common spelling "Tao". The reason for this is that one system of Romanization (examples of which are "Tao Te Ching" and "Lao Tzu") gained almost universal acceptance for a time, then China switched to a different system, and the rest of the world has been trying to catch up ever since. I use this relatively new system, called pinyin, and that is why here you see "Dao De Jing" and "Laozi". It is not really an issue of which system is better, but to the uninitiated, the examples above from the new system are certainly less misleading than those of the old system.

There are several places in this book where C. C. draws what looks like a tiny, gleaming hat. This is actually a depiction of a Chinese ingot—a quantity of precious metal, symbolic here of treasure or wealth.

Many thanks, again, to Professor Lian Xinda for vetting the manuscript and offering numerous useful corrections. Thanks also to Professor Michael LaForge for provding a lucid and enlightening introduction.

—B. B.

The Dao Speaks II
More Whispers of Wisdom

智者的低语——老子说II

老子姓李名耳，字聃。是楚国苦县厉乡曲仁里人，周藏书室的管理人员。

「德」之意五千多字，然后离去，没有人知道他终老于何处。

关令尹喜说：「你将要隐居起来了，请尽力为我著书吧！」于是老子就著述《道德经》上下两篇，谈论「道」与

老子讲修道德，他的学说以自隐无名为主。久住周国，看到周国衰微下去，于是离去，经过函谷关时，

Laozi

According to China's greatest historian Sima Qian:

Laozi's surname was Li, his given name was Er, and his coming-of-age name was Dan.

He was a native of the village of Quren, Li district, Hu county, in the state of Chu, and he worked as caretaker of the imperial archives in Zhou.

Laozi (Lao-tzu) spoke of the Way and the Virtue, focusing on self-efface-ment and not seeking a name for oneself. He resided for a long while in Zhou, and, witnessing the decline of the Zhou empire, he decided to leave. He went west, and when he was about to head out through Hangu pass, Yin Xi the gatekeeper said to him: "Since you are going off to live in reclusion, perhaps you could write down a few of your ideas for me first." So Laozi proceeded to write the Dao De Jing in two books totaling just over 5,000 words. He then departed, and no one knows what became of him.

2

Part I:

The Way

智者的氏吾——老子说 II

谷神不死，是谓玄牝。

玄牝之门，是谓天地根。

绵绵若存，用之不勤。

Chapter 6

The Mysterious Female

1 The Dao exists eternally. It is able to create the myriad things of the world and so is called "the mysterious female".

2 The gate of the mysterious female is the source of the world.

Dao

3 It exists invisibly and forever...

4 And its usefulness is inexhaustible.

Chapter 14

The Dao is Indistinct

Something that is looked at but not seen is called invisible.

1

Something that is listened for but not heard is called inaudible.

2

Something that is groped for but not found is called intangible.

3

Because the Dao is invisible, inaudible, and intangible, it cannot be directly examined, and the three merge into one.

4

視之不見，名曰夷，聽之不聞，名曰希，搏之不得，名曰微。此三者不可致詰，故混而為一。其上不皦，其下不昧，繩繩兮不可名，復歸于無物。是謂無狀之狀，無物之象，是謂惚恍。

智者的低语——老子说II

迎之不见其首，随之不见其后。

执古之道，以御今之有。

能知古始，是谓道纪。

It is neither bright nor dark; it is vague and difficult to describe; it reverts to the immaterial. This is called the formless form. This is called indistinct.

5

Looking up, you do not see its head; following it, you do not see its tail...

6

Dao

Dao

Although the Dao is invisible, inaudible, and intangible, it does indeed exist beyond time and space. Although it is without image or form, it is indeed the master of all things.

If we are able to grasp the ancient Dao, we will be able to manage the things of the present. If we can understand the original conditions, we will understand the laws of the Dao.

7

古之善为道者，微妙玄通，深不可识。夫唯不可识，故强为之容；豫兮若冬涉川；犹兮若畏四邻，俨兮其若客；涣兮其若凌释，敦兮其若朴；旷兮其若谷；混兮其若浊。孰能浊以静之徐清；孰能安以动之徐生。保此道者，不欲盈。夫唯不盈，故能蔽而新成。

其若客；；涣兮若冰之将释；；敦兮其若朴；；旷兮其若谷；；混兮其若浊。

古之善为道者，微妙玄通，深不可识。夫唯不可识，故强为之容；豫兮若冬涉川；；犹兮若畏四邻；；俨兮

In his behavior, he was dignified and courteous, as if a guest in someone's house.

He was also self-diminishing, like ice that has begun to melt.

5

6

His character was simple and unaffected, like an uncarved medium.

His outlook was expansive, and his attitude was one of lowliness, like a deep valley.

7   8

9

His outward expression made him appear mixed-up and foolish and was unrevealing of his abilities, like water that is turbid.

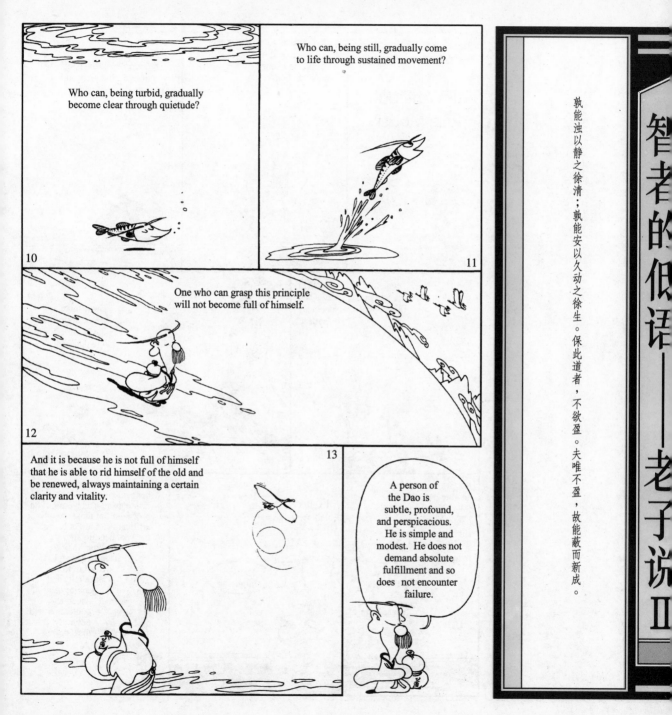

此三者以为文不足，故令有所属：见素抱朴，少私寡欲，绝学无忧。

绝巧弃利，盗贼无有。

绝仁弃义，民复孝慈；

绝圣弃智，民利百倍；

智者的忧吾——老子说 II

Chapter 19

The Artificial Role Model

If you discard the concepts of sageliness and wisdom, the people will benefit a hundred-fold.

1

If you discard the concepts of benevolence and righteousness, the people will return to filial piety and parental compassion.

2

3

If you discard the concepts of cleverness and profit, bandits and thieves will spontaneously disappear.

Sageliness and Wisdom

Benevolence and Righteousness

Cleverness and Profit

These three are mere adornments and insufficient to rule the land.

4

So give the people another pattern to follow: exhibit plainness, embrace simplicity, decrease selfishness, and reduce desires.

5

Exhibit plainness

Pecrease selfishness

Harbor simplicity

Reduce desires

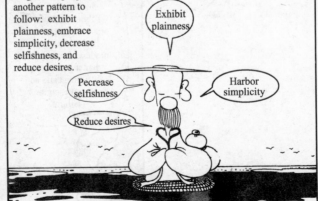

Sageliness and wisdom, benevolence and righteousness, cleverness and profit—all of these are artificial, and not only are they not beneficial to mankind, they are actually harmful. If we return to simplicity and genuineness, all deceit and contention will naturally disappear.

Chapter 21

Reality of the Dao

1 In all actions, people of virtue take the Dao as their standard.

2 This thing the Dao is difficult to pin down. Sometimes it seems to not be there, and sometimes it does...

3 Sometimes it seems to be real, and sometimes it doesn't...

4 It is vague and elusive, yet in this elusiveness it contains all the forms of the universe and includes all things throughout the world.

孔「德」之容，唯「道」是从。「道」之为物，惟恍惟惚。惚兮恍兮，其中有象；恍兮惚兮，其中有物。

智者的低语——老子说Ⅱ

窈兮冥兮，其中有精。其精甚真，其中有信。

自今及古，其名不去，以阅众甫。吾何以知众甫之状哉？以此。

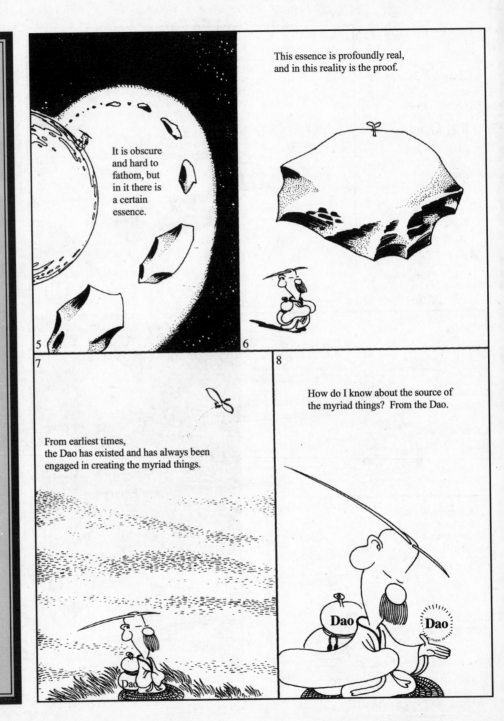

It is obscure and hard to fathom, but in it there is a certain essence.

This essence is profoundly real, and in this reality is the proof.

From earliest times, the Dao has existed and has always been engaged in creating the myriad things.

How do I know about the source of the myriad things? From the Dao.

故飘风不终朝，骤雨不终日。孰为此者？天地。希言自然。

Chapter 23

The Wanton Ruler

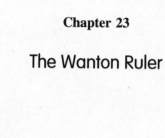

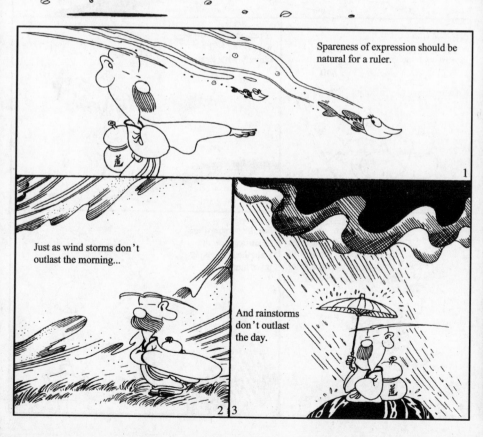

Spareness of expression should be natural for a ruler.

1

Just as wind storms don't outlast the morning...

And rainstorms don't outlast the day.

2 3

「道」者，「道」亦乐得之；同于「德」者，「德」亦乐得之；同于失者，失亦乐得之。

天地尚不能久，而况于人乎？故从事于「道」者，同于「道」；「德」者，同于「德」；失者，同于失。同于

What causes these? Heaven and earth.
If even heaven and earth cannot persist, how can man?

4

A person who works with the Dao will identify with the Dao.

Dao

5

A person who works with virtue will identify with virtue.

Virtue...

6

A person who does not work with the Dao or virtue will identify with neither the Dao nor virtue.

7

For the person who identifies with the Dao, the Dao gladly takes him in;

Dao

8

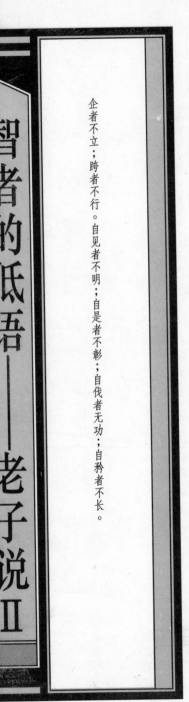

The Exhibitionist

One who stands on tiptoe hoping to gain stature cannot stand steady.

1

One who doubles his strides to get ahead cannot go faster.

2

3 One who sees only with his own eyes does not see clearly.

Look, this essay of mine is fantastic!

Not really!

4 One who thinks he's always right is likely to make errors in judgement.

And there's no doubt in my mind that I'm correct.

Wrong.

Wrong.

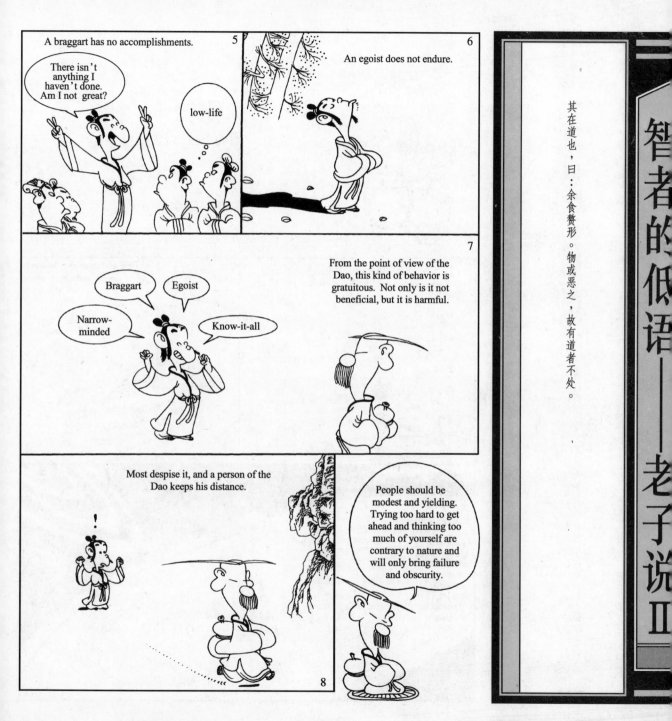

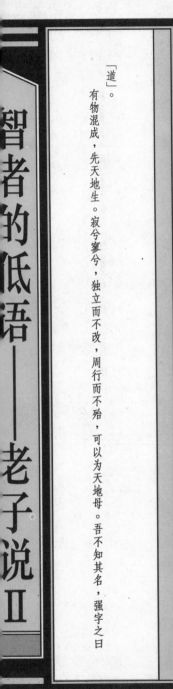

「道」。

有物混成，先天地生。寂兮寥兮，独立而不改，周行而不殆，可以为天地母。吾不知其名，强字之曰

Chapter 25

The Beginning

1 There was something formed from chaos, before the creation of heaven and earth.

2 It is silent and formless. It stands alone always and never ceases coursing.

You could consider it the source of all things. I don't know what it's called, but if forced to name it, I would say "Dao".

Dao

3

4. If forced to describe it, I would say "great". In its greatness, it courses; in its coursing, it travels far.

5. Having traveled far, it returns to stillness and vacuity.

6. So the Dao is great,
Heaven is great,
Earth is great,
And people are also great.
People are one of the four great things in the universe.

7. People follow the earth,
The earth follows heaven,
Heaven follows the Dao,
And the Dao follows spontaneity.

The Dao produced the myriad things, which are ceaselessly changing. Only the Dao is eternal and constant, always functioning. The creation of the myriad things does not happen consciously, but is a spontaneous occurrence—the self-transformation of the myriad things by way of the Dao. In this way, the Dao envelops heaven and earth, endures the passage of time, and supports the myriad things.

人法地，地法天，天法「道」，「道」法自然。

故「道」大，天大，地大，人亦大。域中有四大，而人居其一焉。

强为之名曰「大」。大曰逝，逝曰远，远曰反。

智者的低语——老子说II

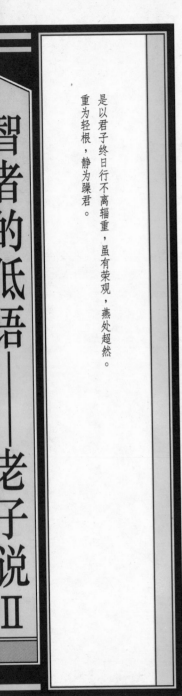

智者的低语——老子说Ⅱ

是以君子终日行不离辎重，虽有荣观，燕处超然。

重为轻根，静为躁君。

Chapter 26

The Serious Ruler

1 Weightiness is the foundation of lightness.

Light

Heavy

2 Quietude is the sovereign of frenzy.

Quiet

Frenzied

3 When traveling, a gentleman never strays far from the heavy wagons,

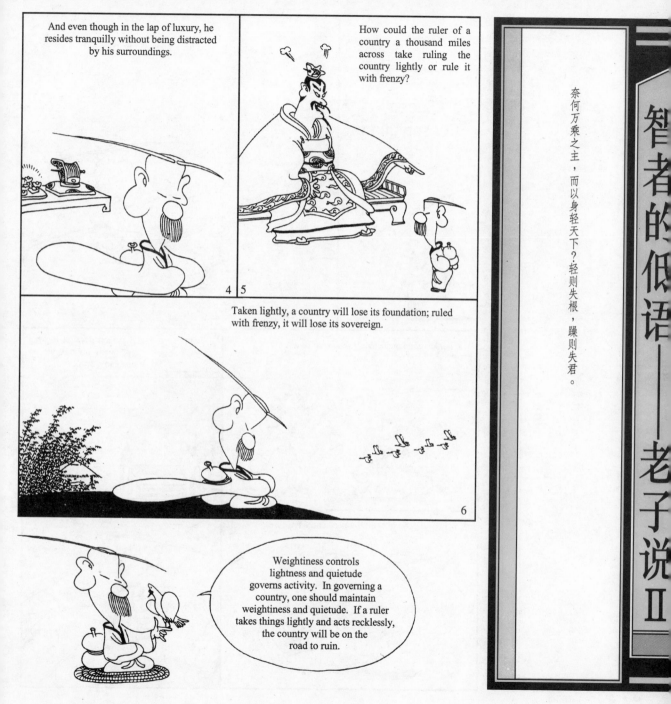

And even though in the lap of luxury, he resides tranquilly without being distracted by his surroundings.

How could the ruler of a country a thousand miles across take ruling the country lightly or rule it with frenzy?

4 5

Taken lightly, a country will lose its foundation; ruled with frenzy, it will lose its sovereign.

6

Weightiness controls lightness and quietude governs activity. In governing a country, one should maintain weightiness and quietude. If a ruler takes things lightly and acts recklessly, the country will be on the road to ruin.

奈何万乘之主，而以身轻天下？轻则失根，躁则失君。

智者的低语——老子说 II

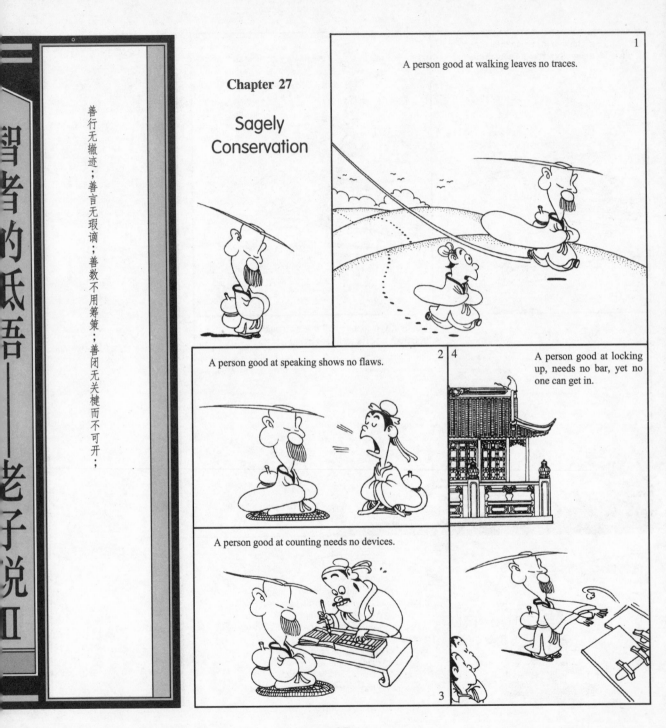

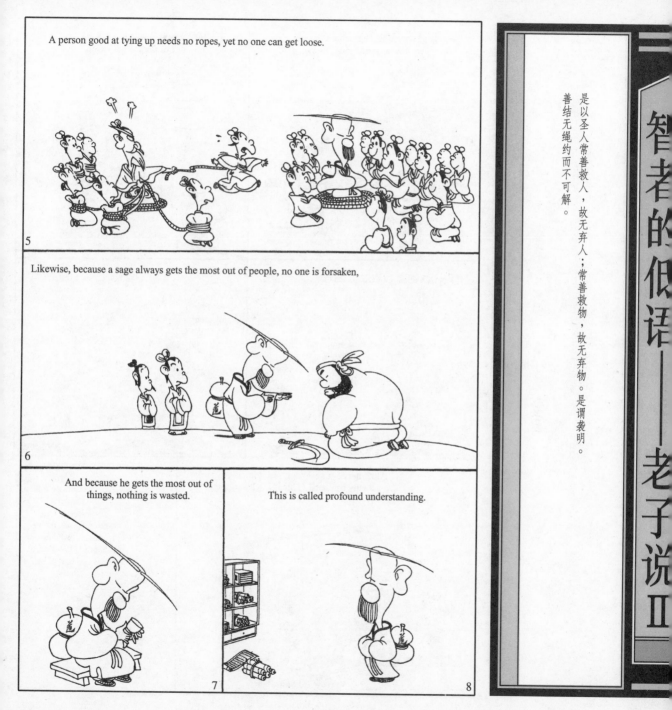

A person good at tying up needs no ropes, yet no one can get loose.

5

Likewise, because a sage always gets the most out of people, no one is forsaken,

6

And because he gets the most out of things, nothing is wasted.

7

This is called profound understanding.

8

是以圣人常善救人，故无弃人；常善救物，故无弃物。是谓袭明。

善结无绳约而不可解。

智者的低语——老子说Ⅱ

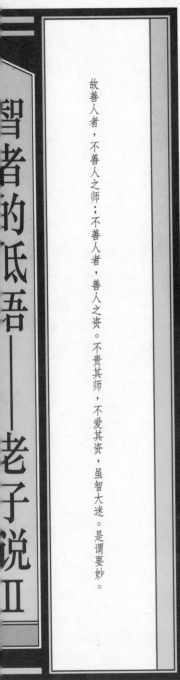

故善人者，不善人之师；不善人者，善人之资。不贵其师，不爱其资，虽智大迷。是谓要妙。

Chapter 28

Confluence of the World

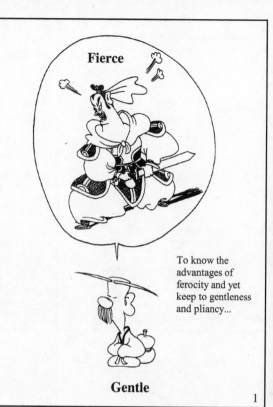

Fierce

To know the advantages of ferocity and yet keep to gentleness and pliancy...

Gentle

1

2 | 3

Is to be the confluence of the world, with all the tributaries flowing to you.

In being the confluence of the world, constant virtue will never leave you, and you will return to the naturalness of infancy.

智者的低语——老子说Ⅱ

知其雄，守其雌，为天下谿。为天下谿，常德不离，复归于婴儿。

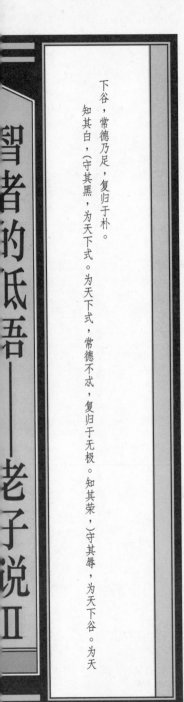

智者的低吾——老子说 II

下谷，常德乃足，复归于朴。

知其白，（守其黑，为天下式。为天下式，常德不忒，复归于无极。知其荣，）守其辱，为天下谷。为天

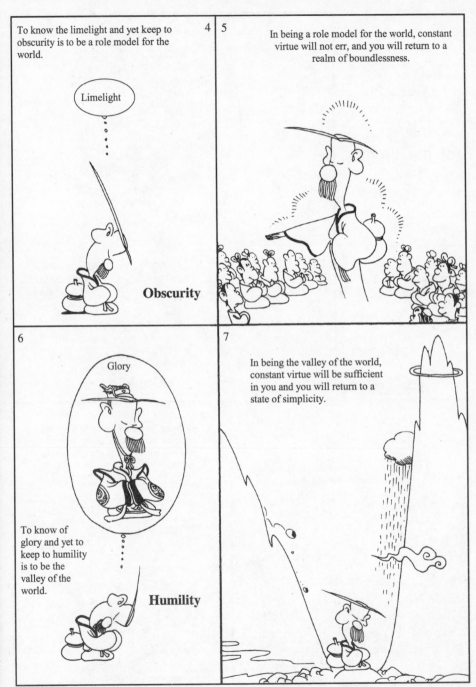

4 5

To know the limelight and yet keep to obscurity is to be a role model for the world.

Limelight

Obscurity

In being a role model for the world, constant virtue will not err, and you will return to a realm of boundlessness.

6 7

Glory

To know of glory and yet to keep to humility is to be the valley of the world.

Humility

In being the valley of the world, constant virtue will be sufficient in you and you will return to a state of simplicity.

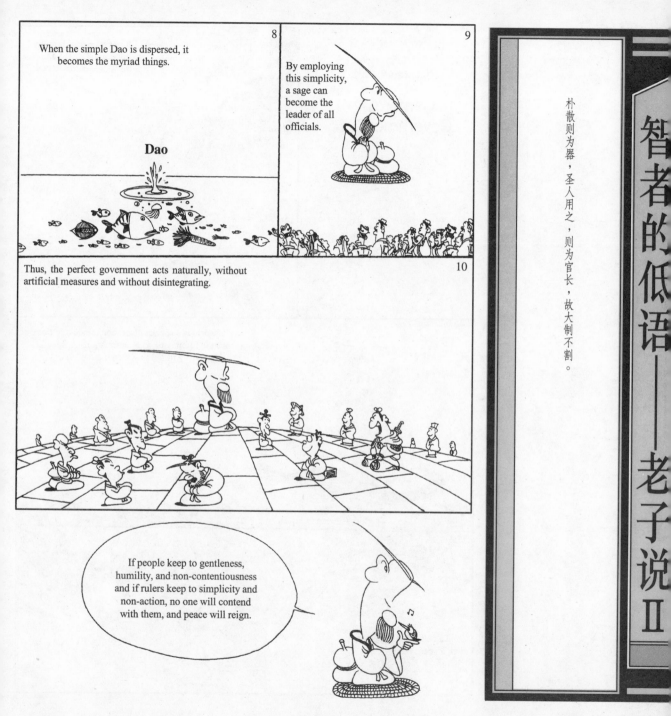

When the simple Dao is dispersed, it becomes the myriad things.

Dao

By employing this simplicity, a sage can become the leader of all officials.

Thus, the perfect government acts naturally, without artificial measures and without disintegrating.

If people keep to gentleness, humility, and non-contentiousness and if rulers keep to simplicity and non-action, no one will contend with them, and peace will reign.

朴散则为器，圣人用之，则为官长，故大制不割。

智者的低语——老子说Ⅱ

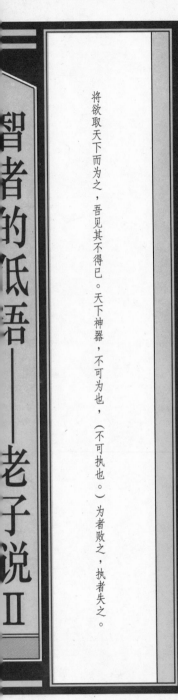

智者的低吾
——老子说 Ⅱ

将欲取天下而为之，吾见其不得已。天下神器，不可为也，（不可执也。）为者败之，执者失之。

Chapter 29

A Natural Government

As for one who tries forcibly to govern the land, I don't think he would succeed.

1

The world is a special place, and things can't be done too forcibly or with domination. A forceful person will fail in governing the land,

2

And a domineering person will lose the land.

3

There are all different kinds of people in the world: some are active while others are passive, some are warm while others are cold, some are firm while others are soft, and some are stable while others are unsteady.

4

5

So in governing the land, a sage must act with respect to human nature and to circumstances;

6

He must govern through non-action and eliminate all extreme measures.

Everything in the world is different, including people, so a ruler must allow for the development of diversity and distinction and must not force things! The ideal government acts in accordance with nature, adjusting to circumstances, abandoning extreme measures, and eliminating harsh policies.

是以圣人去甚，去奢，去泰。

夫物或行或随；或歔或吹；；或强或羸；；或载或隳。

智者的低语——老子说Ⅱ

29

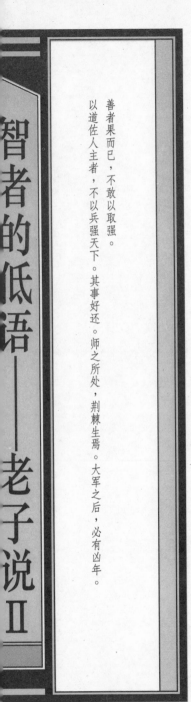

善者果而已，不敢以取强。

以道佐人主者，不以兵强天下。其事好还。师之所处，荆棘生焉。大军之后，必有凶年。

Chapter 30

War and Force

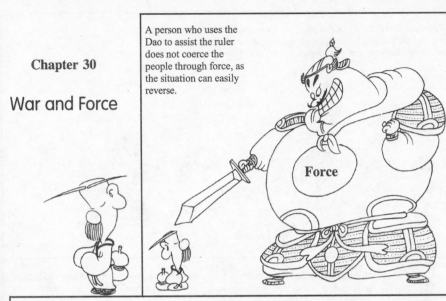

A person who uses the Dao to assist the ruler does not coerce the people through force, as the situation can easily reverse.

Force

1

Wherever the army goes, thorns and brambles spring up. After a great battle, there's sure to be a year of famine.

2

A good general works toward a specific goal then stops, not daring to force the situation.

3

4

He achieves the goal and is not arrogant;
He achieves the goal and does not boast;
He achieves the goal and is not proud.

5

Knowing that the battle was unavoidable, after reaching the goal, there is no need for further action.

6

Strength and force always end up dissolving and so are contrary to the Dao.

7

Anything contrary to the Dao is like a cloudburst and will fizzle out before long.

Nothing humans do is more foolish or cruel than war. Even the victor is badly damaged. In warring, one should not be boastful or arrogant. The battle must be unavoidable, and when the objective met, action must be halted.

物壮则老，是谓不道，不道早已。

果而勿矜，果而勿伐，果而勿骄。果而不得已，果而勿强。

智者的低语——老子说Ⅱ

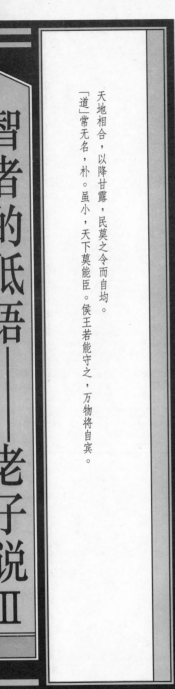

「道」常无名，朴。虽小，天下莫能臣。侯王若能守之，万物将自宾。

天地相合，以降甘露，民莫之令而自均。

Chapter 32

A Natural Balance

1

The Dao is eternally nameless and simple. Though it seems small, nothing in the world can manipulate it.

2

If the kings and princes can keep it, all in the land will pay homage.

Dao

3

When the air of heaven and earth coalesce, sweet dew comes...

4

It is all in balance, without people's interference.

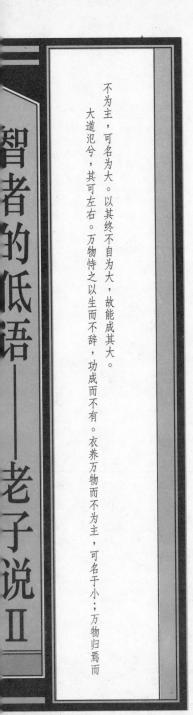

智者的低语——老子说Ⅱ

不为主，可名为大。以其终不自为大，故能成其大。

大道泛兮，其可左右。万物恃之以生而不辞，功成而不有。衣养万物而不为主，可名于小；万物归焉而

Chapter 34

The Dao Nurtures

The Dao flows far and wide, able to go in all directions. The myriad things depend on it for life, yet it doesn't control them. It contributes greatly yet does not demand recognition.

1

To nurture the myriad things without exerting mastery over them is to be known as small.

2

To have the myriad things pay allegiance to it and still not act exert mastery over them is to be known as great.

3

It is its never seeing itself as great...

That proves its greatness.

The Dao gives life to all things and nurtures all things. It allows all things to get what they need and to be themselves. It is its refusal to exert mastery over things that a ruler should emulate.

4

5

Chapter 37

The Natural Ruler

The Dao always acts naturally and so seems to do nothing. In fact, though, nothing is left undone.

1

2

If kings and princes can keep to it, the myriad things will grow and transform on their own.

3

If desires arise from the growth and transformation, we can subdue them through the nameless simplicity of the Dao.

Simplicity

By subduing them through the nameless simplicity of the Dao, the myriad things will be free of selfish desires and will enjoy tranquillity, in which case there will naturally be peace throughout the land.

A ruler should follow nature, and allow the people to develop on their own. If he can cultivate an air of simplicity among the people, he can create peace and stability.

4

朴，夫将不欲。不欲以静，天下将自正。

「道」常无为而无不为。侯王若能守之，万物将自化。化而欲作，吾将镇之以无名之朴。镇之以无名之

智者的低语——老子说Ⅱ

Part II:

The Virtue

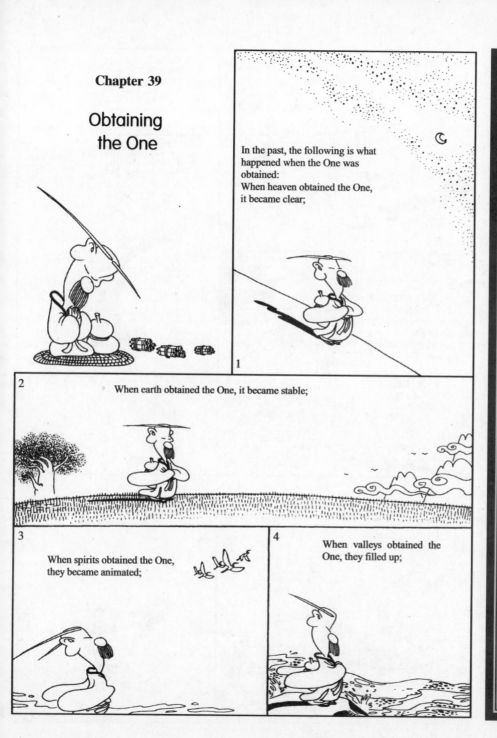

Chapter 39

Obtaining the One

In the past, the following is what happened when the One was obtained:
When heaven obtained the One, it became clear;

1

2 When earth obtained the One, it became stable;

3 When spirits obtained the One, they became animated;

4 When valleys obtained the One, they filled up;

生，侯王得「一」以为天下正。

昔之得「一」者，天得「一」以清，地得「一」以宁，神得「一」以灵，谷得「一」以盈，万物得「一」以

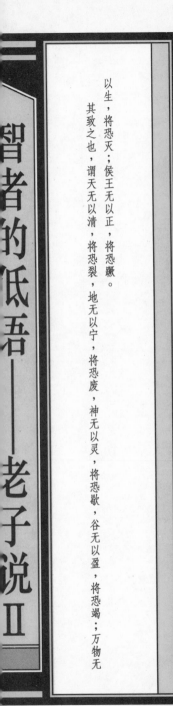

以生，将恐灭；侯王无以正，将恐蹶。

其致之也，谓天无以清，将恐裂，地无以宁，将恐废，神无以灵，将恐歇，谷无以盈，将恐竭；万物无

5 When the myriad things obtained the One, they came to life;

6 When kings and princes obtained the One, the land became ordered. These all happened because the One was obtained.

7 If heaven is not clear, it may crack wide open;

8 If the earth is not stable, it may crumble;

9 If spirits are not animated, they may pass away;

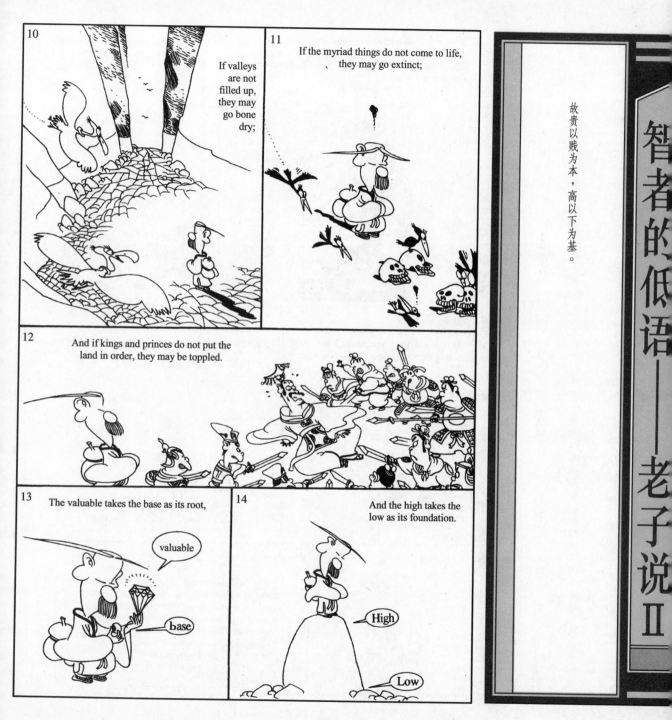

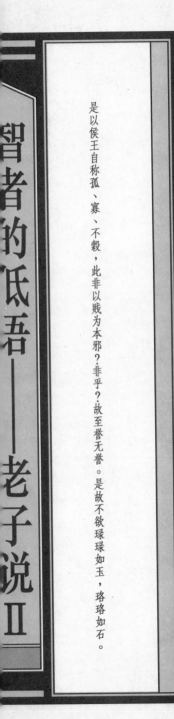

是以侯王自称孤、寡、不穀，此非以贱为本邪？非乎？故至誉无誉。是故不欲琭琭如玉，珞珞如石。

智者的低吾——老子说 II

It is for this reason that kings and princes refer to themselves as "the orphan", "the widower", and "the unfed". Is this not taking the base as a foundation? How can it not be?

Orphan

Widower

Unfed

15

The best praise is no praise, because as soon as there is praise, slander also arises.

16

Do not seek to be like jade or jewels and be paid much attention to by others;

17

But rather be plain like stone and be passed over by others.

18

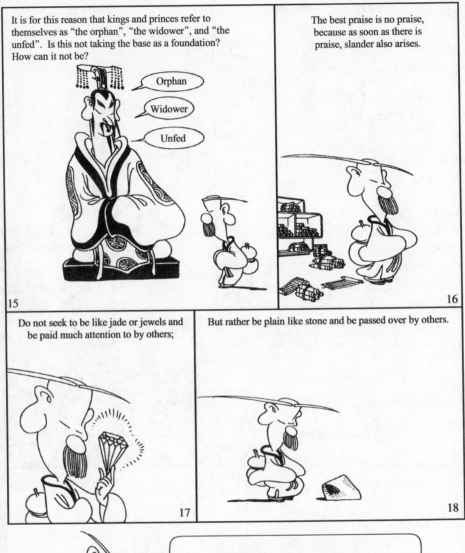

"The One" can be thought of as having been produced by the Dao or as another name for the Dao. All things achieve their greatness through it, and kings and princes achieve their nobility through it. But everything noble is built on a foundation of baseness. Without the base, nothing is noble.

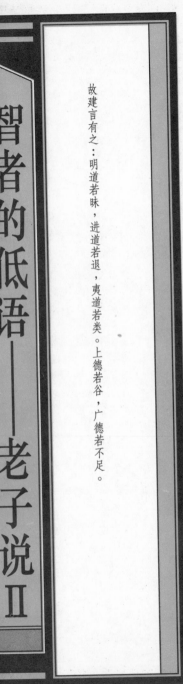

智者的低语——老子说 II

故建言有之：明道若昧，进道若退，夷道若类。上德若谷，广德若不足。

6. "One who understands the Dao is bright inside but appears to be obscure;"

He's not anything worth looking at.

I'll say.

7. "A person of the Dao is humble and self-effacing, and so appears to be retreating;"

8. "The level Dao appears rugged and uneven;"

9. "Highest virtue, being modest and lowly, is like a deep valley;"

10. "Greatest purity appears sullied;"

11. "Extensive virtue appears insufficient;"

建德若偷，质真若渝。

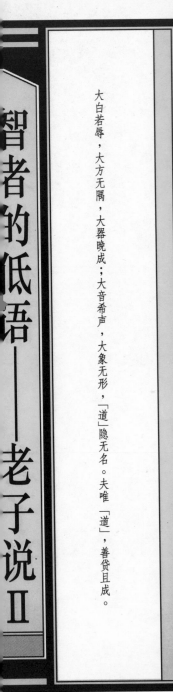

智者的低语——老子说Ⅱ

大白若辱，大方无隅，大器晚成；大音希声，大象无形，「道」隐无名。夫唯「道」，善贷且成。

"The loudest sound can't be heard;"

"The largest form can't be seen;"

16

17

18

"The Dao is invisible and nameless."

19

Only the Dao excels at creating the myriad things and bringing them to maturity.

The interior and exterior of the Dao are completely opposite; its reality and manifestation are completely different. The characteristics of virtue are uncommon, and yet they spring from common sense. Since this is the case, it's no wonder that only the superior person can understand.

Chapter 45

A Model for the World

1 The most complete thing seems to be lacking, yet its usefulness is never-ending.

2 The most replete thing seems to be empty, yet its usefulness is inexhaustible.

3 The straightest of things appears bent,

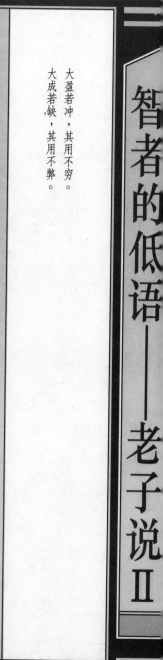

智者的低语——老子说 II

大盈若冲，其用不穷。

大成若缺，其用不弊。

静胜躁，寒胜热。清静为天下正。

大直若屈，大巧若拙，大辩若讷。

The most agile of things appears clumsy,

And the greatest eloquence appears inarticulate.

4

5

6 Quietude overcomes frenzy; cold overcomes heat.

So tranquil.

7 Tranquil non-action can be a model for the world.

A perfect character is not exhibited on the outside, but is concealed on the inside. The substance of the Dao is empty and quiet, yet the functioning of the Dao can overcome restlessness and activity. If we are good at quietude, non-action, non-interference, and following nature, then we can be models for the rest of the world.

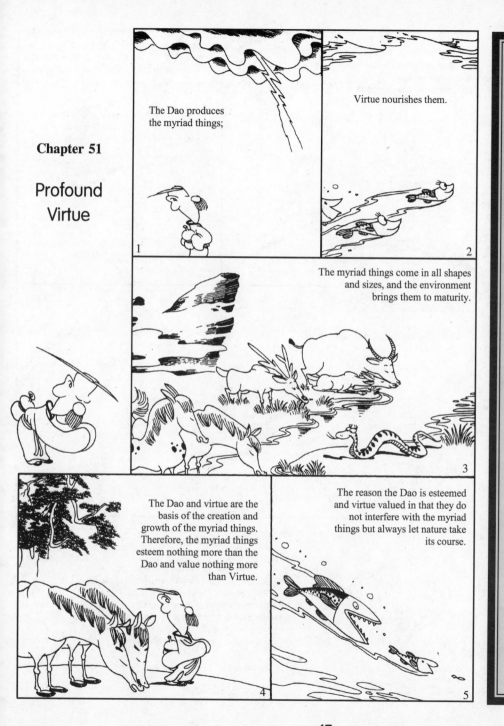

Chapter 51

Profound Virtue

1 The Dao produces the myriad things;

2 Virtue nourishes them.

3 The myriad things come in all shapes and sizes, and the environment brings them to maturity.

4 The Dao and virtue are the basis of the creation and growth of the myriad things. Therefore, the myriad things esteem nothing more than the Dao and value nothing more than Virtue.

5 The reason the Dao is esteemed and virtue valued in that they do not interfere with the myriad things but always let nature take its course.

智者的低语——老子说Ⅱ

「道」之尊，「德」之贵，夫莫之命而常自然。

是以万物莫不尊「道」而贵「德」。

「道」生之，「德」畜之，物形之，势成之。

47

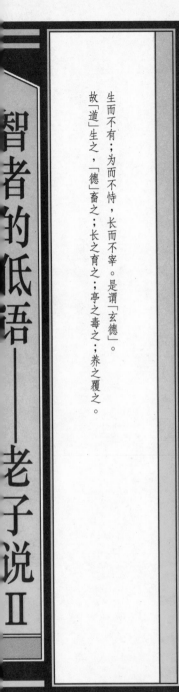

生而不有；为而不恃，长而不宰。是谓「玄德」。

故「道」生之，「德」畜之；长之育之；亭之毒之；养之覆之。

The Dao produces them, while virtue fosters them, allows them to grow, nurtures them, brings them to maturity, and protects them.

6

Producing without taking as one's own, nurturing without presuming upon one's abilities, bringing to maturity without trying to control...

7

This is the most profound virtue.

8

The Dao and virtue create the myriad things but entirely with spontaneity as the basis. They do not control or interfere with them, just allowing them to develop naturally. The greatness of the Dao and virtue lies in this lack of selfishness and desire, and it is why they are held in high regard by the myriad things.

Chapter 52

The Doors
of
Perception

If there was a beginning to the world, it can be considered the mother of the world.

Dao 道

1

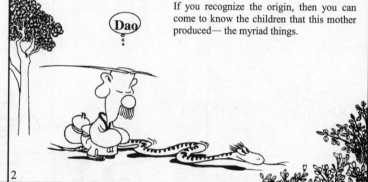

Dao

If you recognize the origin, then you can come to know the children that this mother produced— the myriad things.

2

If you can recognize the children, and if you can maintain the Dao of the mother of the myriad things, you will never come to harm.

3

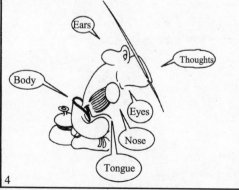

If you can close the passageways and doors of desire, not allowing desire to arise, you will be untroubled your whole life.

Ears

Thoughts

Body

Eyes

Nose

Tongue

4

天下有始，以为天下母。既得其母，以知其子；既知其子，复守其母，没身不殆。

智者的低语——老子说 II

49

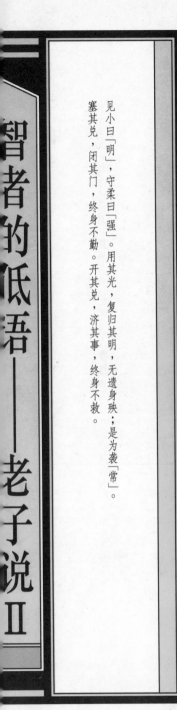

见小曰「明」，守柔曰「强」。用其光，复归其明，无遗身殃；是为袭「常」。

塞其兑，闭其门，终身不勤。开其兑，济其事，终身不救。

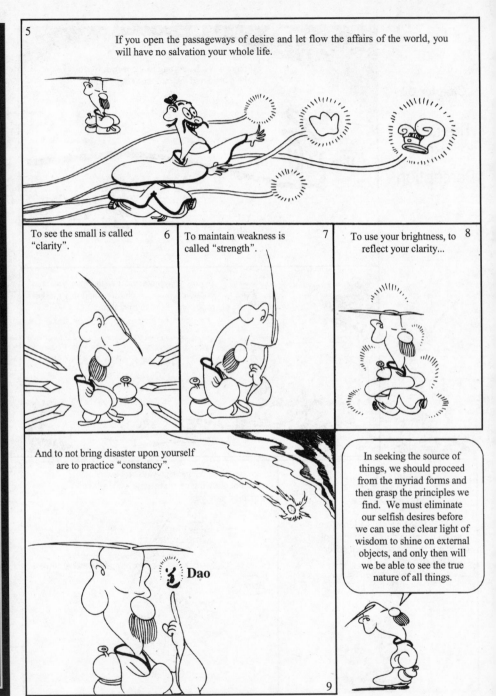

5
If you open the passageways of desire and let flow the affairs of the world, you will have no salvation your whole life.

6
To see the small is called "clarity".

7
To maintain weakness is called "strength".

8
To use your brightness, to reflect your clarity...

And to not bring disaster upon yourself are to practice "constancy".

Dao

9

In seeking the source of things, we should proceed from the myriad forms and then grasp the principles we find. We must eliminate our selfish desires before we can use the clear light of wisdom to shine on external objects, and only then will we be able to see the true nature of all things.

Chapter 53

The Great Path

1. If I were walking along a great path that I was only slightly familiar with,

2. All I would fear would be going astray.

3. The great Dao is level, yet people prefer the by-ways.

4. The court is so very chaotic,

   Say it!

   Take that!

5. The fields so very barren,

51

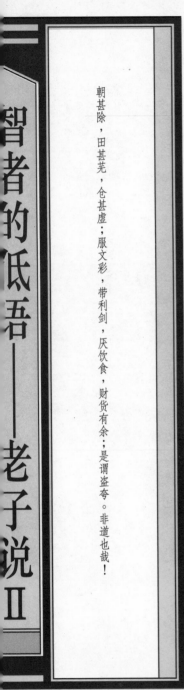

智者的低吾——老子说Ⅱ

朝甚除，田甚芜，仓甚虚；服文彩，带利剑，厌饮食，财货有余；是谓盗夸。非道也哉！

Chapter 54

Cultivating Virtue

1. One who excels in establishing will not be plucked out;

Virture

2. One who excels in embracing will not be pulled away.

Virtue

3. If you establish and embrace virtue, not only will you enjoy good fortune, but your descendants will honor you forever.

4. This virtue must be present in all you do.

5. If you cultivate your body with it, your virtue will be genuine;

下，其德乃普。

修之于身，其德乃真；修之于家，其德乃余；修之于乡，其德乃长；修之于邦，其德乃丰；修之于天

善建者不拔，善抱者不脱，子孙以祭祀不辍。

智者的低语——老子说II

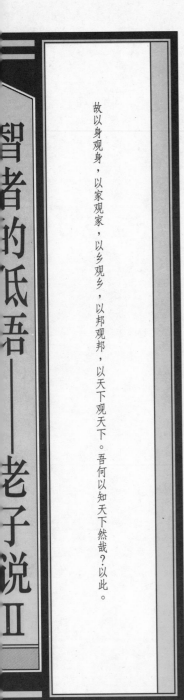

故以身观身，以家观家，以乡观乡，以邦观邦，以天下观天下。吾何以知天下然哉？以此。

Chapter 55

An Infant's Virtue

One who has an abundance of virtue is like an innocent babe.

1

Hee hee!

2
An infant is ignorant, weak, and helpless, a little ball of pure nature, so harmful creatures don't sting it,

3
Vicious beasts don't maul it, and birds of prey don't seize it.

4
Although it's flesh and bones are soft, it's grip is firm.

知和曰「常」，知常曰「明」。益生曰祥。心使气曰强。
未知牝牡之合而全作，精之至也。终日号而不嗄，和之至也。

Although it doesn't yet know the union of male and female, its organ rises. This is because its essence is complete.

5

It can cry and scream all day without becoming hoarse. This is because its inner harmony is complete.

Wah!

6

To understand this principle of gentleness is to be in accord with the constant Dao. To understand the constant Dao is to be enlightened.

7

8

If you don't understand the constant Dao and instead indulge your desires and nurture life too much, you will bring disaster upon yourself.

To hasten nature because of your desires is to seek strength,

But upon reaching the strength of maturity, everything goes into decline.

Strength is not in accord with the Dao, and things not in accord with the Dao soon perish.

9

10

11

When people are just born, they are without knowledge or desire. You could say that this is when their virtue is most abundant. When they have grown up, their interests and desires increase daily, as does their hypocrisy, and gradually they lose the Dao and Virtue.

A person who has attained the Dao is as soft and weak, pure and innocent as and infant, yet he is full of vitality and natural and carefree in every way.

智者的低语——老子说 II

物壮则老，谓之不道，不道早已。

祸兮，福之所倚；福兮，祸之所伏。孰知其极？
其政闷闷，其民淳淳；其政察察，其民缺缺。

Chapter 58

There Is No Justice

1 If a ruler governs through non-action and non-interference, then the people will be simple;

2 If a ruler is always intent on something and interferes all the time, then the people will be cunning.

3 Concealed inside disaster is good fortune;

Disaster

Good fortune

4 Hidden beneath good fortune lurks disaster. Who knows when one will give rise to the other.

Good fortune

Disaster

Panel 5: There is no justice! Justice reverts to injustice, and goodness reverts to evil.

Justice ⇆ Injustice
Goodness ⇆ Evil

Panel 6: Goodness

Evil

People are confused and have been for so long.

Panel 7: Although Sages are square, they do not scrape people;

Panel 8: Although they are sharp, they do not cut people;

Panel 9: Although they are direct, they are not careless;

Panel 10: Although they are bright, they are not blinding.

Good fortune and disaster are not stable, justice and injustice are not fair, good and bad have no standard. Because most people don't understand this, they see the face of things, but are not able to enter deeper and see the other side. As a result, they seek good fortune but get disaster.

是以圣人方而不割，廉而不刿，直而不肆，光而不耀。

其无正也。正复为奇，善复为妖。人之迷，其日固久。

智者的低语——老子说 II

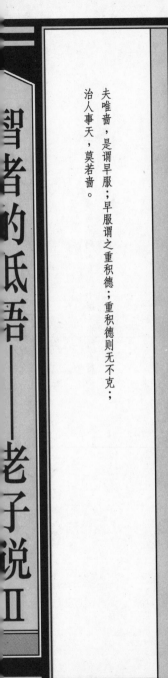

智者的低吾——老子说Ⅱ

夫唯嗇，是謂早服；早服謂之重積德；重積德則無不克；

治人事天，莫若嗇。

Chapter 59

Frugality

In governing people and nurturing life, nothing is better than frugality.

1

Only in frugality can you get right to following the Dao.

Dao

2

Getting right to following the Dao is to accumulate much virtue.

Virtue

3

I do nothing, and nothing is left undone...

With an accumulation of much virtue, so that you are tranquil, non-active, and natural, there will be nothing that you cannot overcome;

4

5

When there is nothing that you cannot overcome, your power will be beyond measure;

6

When your power is beyond measure, you can take up the responsibilities of protecting a country;

Governing through non-action

无为而治

And when you take up the responsibilities of protecting a country in this way, you can endure. This is called "establishing deep roots and solid stalks", and it is the principle of "an enduring life and lasting vision".

7

Only through frugality can you cultivate your natural potential, accumulate energy, bring out ability, and preserve your life within, while also achieving a realm of purity and simplicity.

Dao

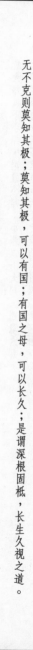

无不克则莫知其极；莫知其极，可以有国；有国之母，可以长久；是谓深根固柢，长生久视之道。

智者的低语——老子说 II

61

智者的低吾——老子说Ⅱ

故大邦以下小邦，则取小邦；小邦以下大邦，则取大邦。
大邦者下流，天下之牝。天下之交也。牝常以静胜牡，以静为下。

Chapter 61

The Lowly Superpower

1 A large country is like a body of water in that it abides in lowliness—it is the confluence of all the world.

2 It resides in all that is feminine in the world. The female uses quietude to win over the male and it is in this quietude that she is lowly.

3 A large country takes a position below smaller countries and thereby gains the allegiance of smaller countries. A small country takes a position below larger countries, and thereby is taken in by larger countries.

4

One uses humility to win the allegiance of the other,
And one uses humility to win the acceptance of the other.

5

The larger country wishes for no more than to care for the smaller country, while the smaller country wishes for no more than to serve the larger country. In this way, both the large and small countries get what they desire, and it is why the large country in particular should be humble.

6

Through humility, the small country is merely able to keep itself intact, while the large country brings all people to pay allegiance to it.

The principles of interaction among large and small countries should be humility and pliancy. If instead they take firm, contentious attitudes, the small country is sure to perish, and the large country will not easily endure.

故或下以取，或下而取。大邦不过欲兼畜人，小邦不过欲入事人。夫两者各得所欲，大者宜为下。

智者的低语——老子说II

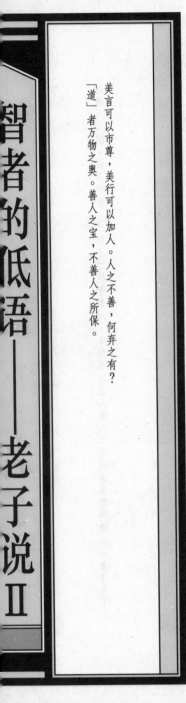

智者的低语——老子说 II

「道」者万物之奥。善人之宝，不善人之所保。

美言可以市尊，美行可以加人。人之不善，何弃之有？

Chapter 62

Prizing the Dao

1. The Dao is the treasury of the myriad things, and the treasure of the good person.

Dao

2. The principle of life...

Dao

A bad person also seeks to protect it rather than defy it.

3. A person who cultivates the Dao is an impressive speaker and can thereby win the respect of others. He also performs impressive deeds and so is accepted by others. Why would a bad person forsake the Dao?

Dao

Therefore, when an emperor is crowned or the three dukes invested, presenting a jade disk followed by a team of horses is not as good as presenting the Dao itself.

4

Dao

Why did the ancients so prize the Dao?

5

Isn't it said: "With it one attains what one seeks. With it, one's transgressions are pardoned?" For this reason, it is the prize of all the land.

For a ruler to have a mind of tranquillity and non-action that allows him to follow the Dao is much more important than having a jade disk and a team of horses.

6

古之所以贵此道者何？不曰：求以得，有罪以免邪？故为天下贵。

故立天子，置三公，虽有拱璧以先驷马，不如坐进此道。

智者的低语——老子说Ⅱ

65

智者的低语——老子说 II

图难于其易，为大于其细；天下难事，必作于易，天下大事，必作于细。

为无为，事无事，味无味。

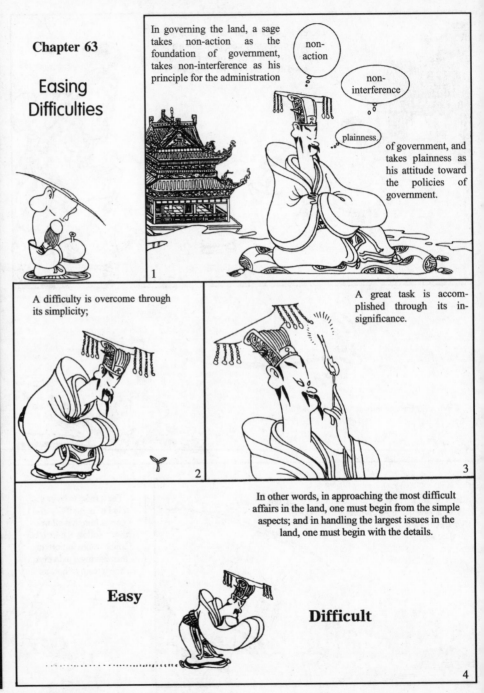

Chapter 63

Easing Difficulties

1

In governing the land, a sage takes non-action as the foundation of government, takes non-interference as his principle for the administration

non-action

non-interference

plainness

of government, and takes plainness as his attitude toward the policies of government.

2

A difficulty is overcome through its simplicity;

3

A great task is accomplished through its insignificance.

In other words, in approaching the most difficult affairs in the land, one must begin from the simple aspects; and in handling the largest issues in the land, one must begin with the details.

Easy

Difficult

4

老子说 II — 智者的低语

智者的低语——老子说 II

夫轻诺必寡信：多易必多难。是以圣人犹难之，故终无难矣。

是以圣人终不为大，故能成其大。

为之于未有，治之于未乱。

其安易持，其未兆易谋。其脆易泮，其微易散。

Chapter 64

Planning and Perseverance

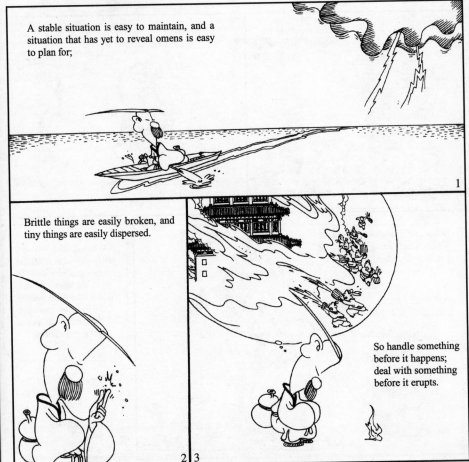

A stable situation is easy to maintain, and a situation that has yet to reveal omens is easy to plan for;

1

Brittle things are easily broken, and tiny things are easily dispersed.

So handle something before it happens; deal with something before it erupts.

2 3

A tree that you can barely embrace began from a tiny sprout;

A nine story tower began as a pile of dirt;

A thousand mile journey begins with a single step.

When people do things, they often go part way then fail. But if you can be as careful at the end as you are at the beginning, you will never fail.

The ordinary mind

In whatever you do, proceed from the small to the large, from the near to the distant. In large and laborious tasks, you must work with persistence and patience. If you slack off just a bit, you are likely to fall just that much short of your goal.

4

5

6

7

智者的低语——老子说 II

民之从事，常于几成而败之。慎终如始，则无败事。

合抱之木，生于毫末；九层之台，起于累土；千里之行，始于足下。

智者的低吾——老子说Ⅱ

古之善为道者，非以明民，将以愚之。

民之难治，以其智多。故以智治国，国之贼；不以智治国，国之福。

Mysterious Virtue

1

The ancients who excelled at employing the Dao in governing, did not strive to make the people intelligent and cunning, but to make them simple and generous.

How am I going to keep them in line...

The reason people became difficult to govern is that they became too intelligent and cunning.

We gotta fight the government...

2

So governing through cunning means will ensure disaster. Not governing through cunning means is the good fortune of a country.

3

The difference between these two ways of governing is an important principle to be maintained. Understanding and practicing this principle is called "mysterious virtue".

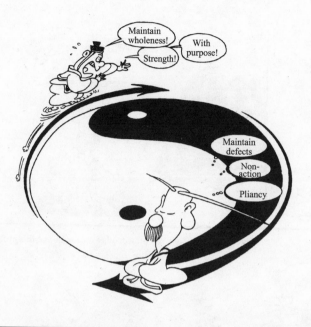

This mysterious virtue is profound and far-reaching! It returns with all things, and by following it, you will join the great flow of nature.

知此两者亦稽式。常知稽式，是谓「玄德」，「玄德」深矣，远矣，与物反矣，然后乃至大顺。

智者的低语——老子说Ⅱ

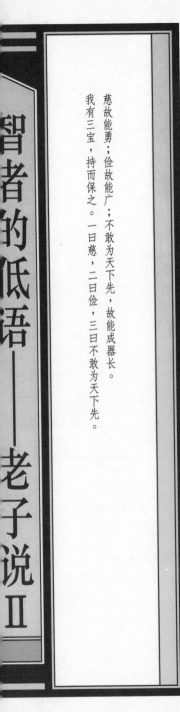

我有三宝，持而保之。一曰慈，二曰俭，三曰不敢为天下先。

慈故能勇；；俭故能广；不敢为天下先，故能成器长。

Chapter 67

The Three Treasures

I have three treasures. I keep and protect them. The first is called "compassion". The second is called "frugality". The third is called "an unwillingness to be first".

Frugal

Compassionate

Unwilling to be first

1

With compassion, one can protect other creatures, and this produces courage.

Waa!

2

With frugality, one can nurture the spirit and store up virtue, and these can be extended far and wide.

Nurture the spirit.

Store up virtue.

3

With an unwillingness to be first, one gains the respect of others and can therefore act as leader.

Humble and yielding.

He's just being modest. He's actually very capable!

4

智者的低语——老子说 II

夫慈，以战则胜，以守则固。天将救之，以慈卫之。

今舍慈且勇；舍俭且广；舍后且先；死矣！

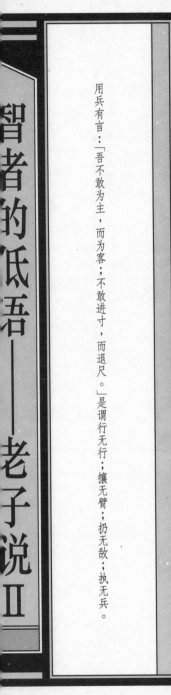

用兵有言：「吾不敢为主，而为客；不敢进寸，而退尺。」是谓行无行；攘无臂；扔无敌；执无兵。

Chapter 69

Warfare

Although you have weapons, give the appearance that you do not;

Always maintain a compassionate and non-contentious attitude.

5

6

There is no greater disaster than underestimating an enemy.

Power

If we underestimate the enemy, we could lose our three treasures.

Blam!

7

8

9

When two forces battle, the compassionate one will be victorious.

War should only occur as a last resort. When it must be faced, do not provoke, do not invade, and do not underestimate the enemy. And do not blithely go into battle.

智者的低语——老子说 II

祸莫大于轻敌，轻敌几丧吾宝。故抗兵相若，哀者胜矣。

75

言有宗，事有君。夫唯无知，是以不我知。

天下莫能知，莫能行。

吾言甚易知，甚易行。

Chapter 70

Heart of Jade

My words are very easy to understand, and very easy to practice.

But because everyone is blinded by selfish desires and confused by fame and wealth, no one is able to understand or practice them.

Profit

Wealth

desires

desires

Fame

desires

There is a source for my words; there is a basis for my actions.

1

2

3

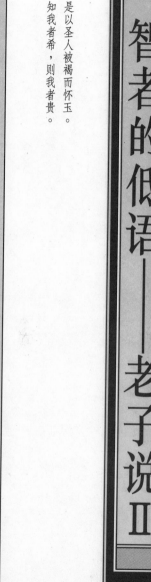

 智者的低语——老子说Ⅱ

夫唯不厌，是以不厌。
无狎其所居，无厌其所生。
民不畏威，则大威至。

Chapter 72

Tyranny

1 When the people no longer fear a tyrant's oppression...

2 An even greater calamity is immanent.

Therefore, do not exploit the people's livelihood,

We have no rice left!

Hand it over! **3**

Do not oppress the people's lives.

4

Because the sage neither exploits nor oppresses the people, they do not turn on him, but rather turn toward him.

5

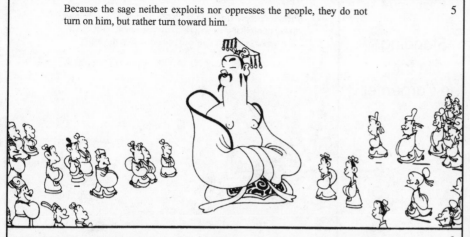

The sage understands himself but does not display himself. He cares about himself but does not glorify himself.

6

Therefore, discard all thought of displaying and glorifying yourself, and simply understand and care for yourself.

7

When a tyrannical government oppresses the people's freedom and livelihood so that the people can no longer live comfortably and in peace, they will risk everything and revolt.

故去彼取此。
是以圣人自知不自见；自爱不自贵。

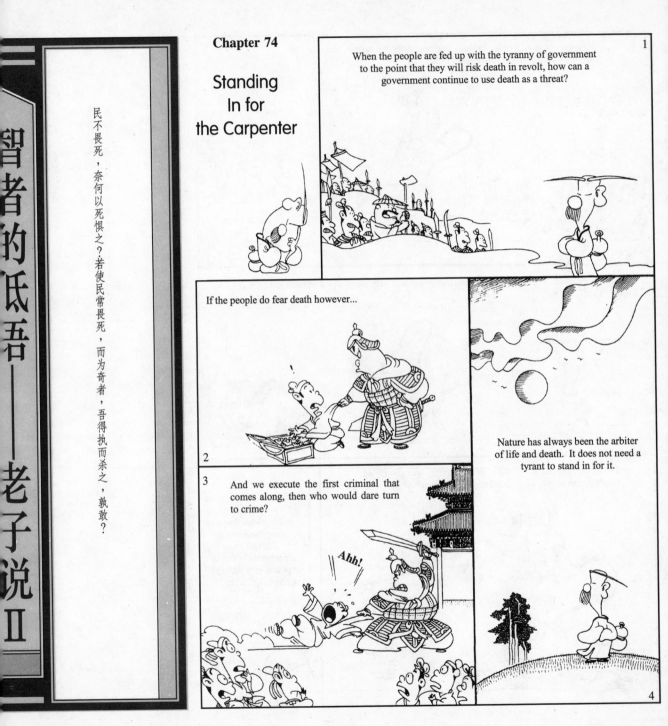

民不畏死，奈何以死惧之？若使民常畏死，而为奇者，吾得执而杀之，孰敢？

智者的低吾——老子说 II

Chapter 74

**Standing
In for
the Carpenter**

When the people are fed up with the tyranny of government to the point that they will risk death in revolt, how can a government continue to use death as a threat?

If the people do fear death however...

And we execute the first criminal that comes along, then who would dare turn to crime?

Ahh!

Nature has always been the arbiter of life and death. It does not need a tyrant to stand in for it.

80

常有司杀者杀。夫代司杀者杀，是谓代大匠斲，夫代大匠斲者，希有不伤其手矣。

智者的低语——老子说 II

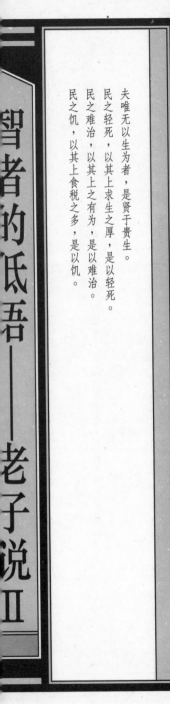

智者的低语——老子说 II

夫唯无以生为者，是贤于贵生。

民之轻死，以其上求生之厚，是以轻死。

民之难治，以其上之有为，是以难治。

民之饥，以其上食税之多，是以饥。

Chapter 75

Starvation and Taxes

People go hungry because food taxes are too high.

> If you take anymore we'll starve to death!

1

People are difficult to govern because rulers often do too much.

> They issue one order in the morning, then change it in the evening. How are we supposed to keep up?

2

People take death lightly because their rulers pursue lavish lives.

> We can't make a living anyway, so we'd rather take them down with us!

3

Thus, a more enlightened ruler will govern quietly and without desires, rather than pursue too much.

4

Exploitation and oppression are the roots of political chaos. When rulers are tyrannical, the people will rise up from the edge of starvation and death to fight back.

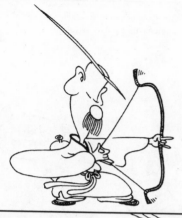

Chapter 77

The Drawn Bow

1
Isn't the law of nature like a drawn bow?

2
If the bow is too high, you lower it;

3
If it is too low, you raise it;

4
If the string is too long, you shorten it; If it is too short, you lengthen it.

天之道，损有余而补不足。

人之道，则不然，损不足以奉有余。

孰能有余以奉天下？唯有道者。

The law of nature reduces surplus and supplements any insufficiency in the world.

Unlike the laws of society, which reduce insufficiency and supplement surplus.

He's taking from the poor to give to the rich!

This is for you.

Ooo, thank you.

Who can take a surplus and supplement the insufficiencies of the world?

Only a person of the Dao.

The laws of nature redistribute things in order to maintain an equilibrium. Only by emulating nature and seeking this kind of equilibrium can society achieve harmony.

Chapter 80

The Ideal Country

The ideal country is as follows: A small area of land and a small number of people.

I'll have a pound of tangerines, please.

1

There are no conflicts, so even though there are all kinds of weapons, they go unused.

2

The government is not tyrannical, so the people needn't move far away.

3

There are boats and carts, but no one needs to use them.

4

Although there are armor and weapons, there is no need to display them.

I've wasted fifty years as a soldier. I've never even gotten to go to battle.

5

民复结绳而用之。

小国寡民。使有什伯之器而不用；使民重死而不远徙。虽有舟舆，无所乘之；虽有甲兵，无所陈之。使

甘其食，美其服，安其居，乐其俗。

The people return to the old ways and use knots to record things.

6

People are simple and without desires, so although everyone eats plain food, it tastes delicious;

7

Although they wear coarse clothing, it looks beautiful;

8

Although they live in humble dwellings, they are comfortable;

9

And although the customs are simple, the people are very happy.

10

They see the people of neighboring countries and can even hear their chickens and dogs,

11

12

but because the people lead simple lives and have few needs, they live to an old age without ever going to visit other countries.

In a small country with a small population, social order can be maintained without suppression, depending instead on the goodness of the simple populace. Because there are no catastrophes resulting from war nor an atmosphere of violence, the people are honest and trustworthy. Because the people have no worries of instability and no fear of loss, they can live in simplicity, peace, and happiness.

邻国相望，鸡犬之声相闻，民至老死，不相往来。

智者的低语——老子说Ⅱ

图字：01－2005－0834

图书在版编目（CIP）数据

老子说 Ⅱ ＝ The Dao Speaks Ⅱ：More Whispers of Wis-dom/蔡志忠绘．—北京：现代出版社，2005
ISBN 7-80188-513-9

Ⅰ．老… Ⅱ．蔡… Ⅲ．漫画-作品集-中国-现代 Ⅳ．J228.2

中国版本图书馆 CIP 数据核字（2005）第 025585 号

The Dao Speaks Ⅱ :More Whispers of Wisdom
老子说Ⅱ:智者的低语

作者/〔台湾〕蔡志忠
译者/〔美〕Brian Bruya
总策划/吴江江
责任编辑/张　璐
封面设计/刘　刚
出版发行/现代出版社(北京安外安华里 504 号　邮编:100011)
印刷/北京平谷早立印刷厂
开本/880×1230　1/24　4 印张
版次/2005 年 5 月第 1 版
　　　2005 年 5 月第 1 次印刷
印数/1～6000 册
书号/ISBN 7-80188-513-9
定价/9.80 元